How to Hide a Parakeet

& other birds

A Grosset & Dunlap **ALL ABOARD BOOK**®

With special thanks to
Stephen F. Bailey, Ph.D.
Department of Ornithology
California Academy of Sciences

If
you take
a careful look,
you'll see
how
creatures
in this book
are
CAMOUFLAGED
and out
of view—
although
they're
right
in
front
of
you.

RUTH HELLER'S

How to Hide a Parakeet

&

other birds

Originally published as How to Hide a Whip-poor-will & Other Birds

Grosset & Dunlap, Publishers

At
night
the
WHIP-POOR-WILL
is
heard
because
it's
a
nocturnal
bird.

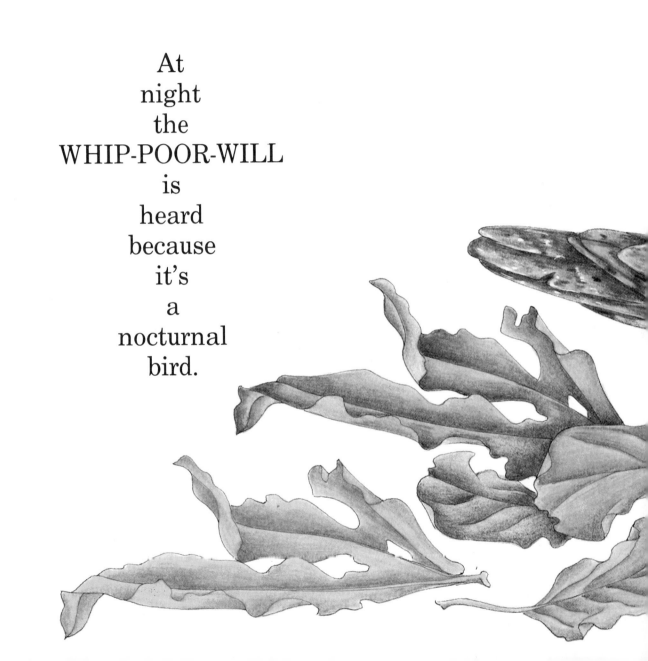

By day it rests
upon the ground
and cannot easily…

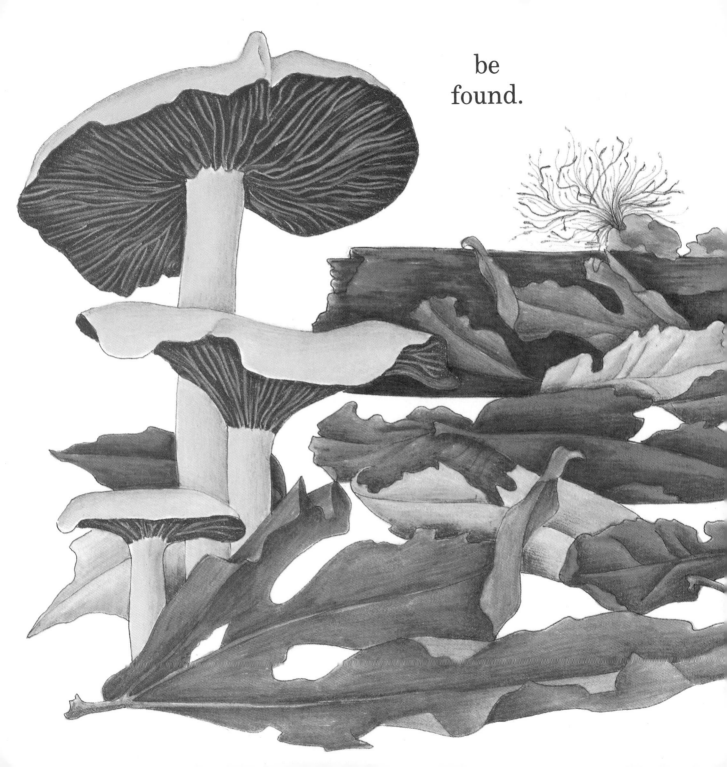

be
found.

Nocturnal,
too,
is
the
POTOO,
who
in
the
jungle
likes
to
doze
in…

an
upright,
rigid
pose.

At
dawn
the
SCREECH
OWL...

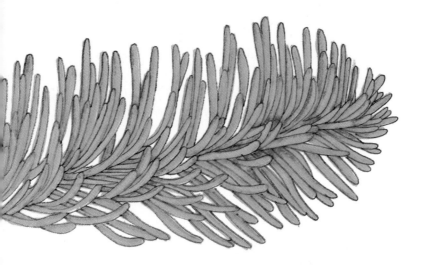

shuts
its
eyes
and
then
is
hard
to
recognize.

In
its
tropical retreat,
this
PLUM-HEADED
PARAKEET...

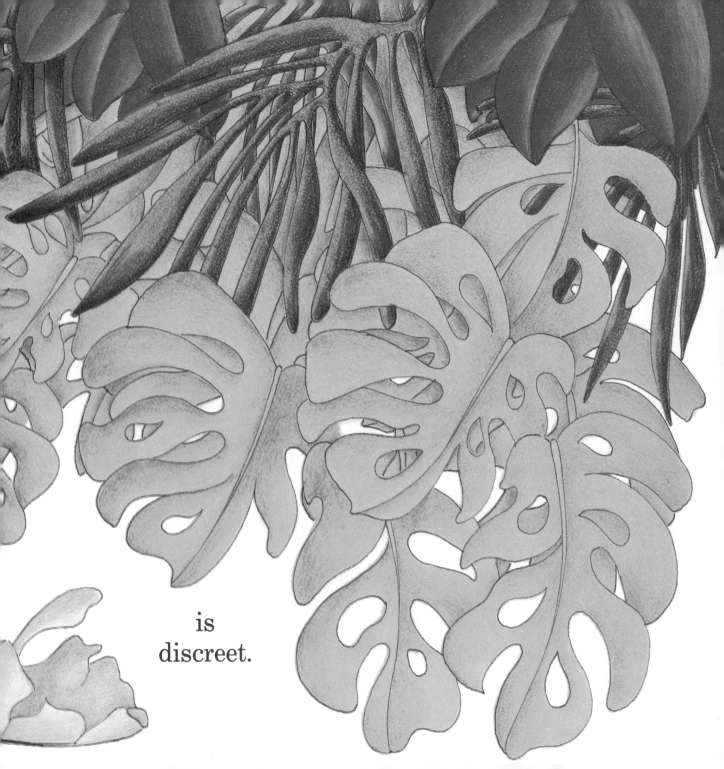

is
discreet.

With
stripes
upon
her
neck and breast,
a
BITTERN,
sitting
on her nest,
sways
with the reeds
as they are
blowing…

so
that
she
is
barely
showing.

When
seen beside her
ornate
mate,
this
WOOD DUCK
may not
look
first-rate,

but
while
all
eyes
are
watching
him...

she is roosting
on
a
limb.

The
PLOVER
doesn't
build
a
nest.

Her
eggs
are
unprotected.
They...

look just like the rocks
nearby and so go
undetected.

Because the world is
hostile,
all creatures need
protection.
They need to hide
so thoroughly
that they defy detection.

So…
some of them use
camouflage
to fade away with ease
from predators
who like to dine
upon these predatees.

But…
predators
to live must eat,
so
also fade and are
discreet,
and then their prey
on which they sup
can't see
who's going
to eat them up.